CUT, COLOR & PASTE
BIBLE WORKERS

Janet Miller

To my family: Earl, Bill, Heather, Amanda and Elaine.

CUT, COLOR AND PASTE: BIBLE WORKERS
©2000 by Rainbow Publishers
ISBN 1-885358-82-2
Rainbow reorder# RB38062

Rainbow Publishers
P.O. Box 261129
San Diego, CA 92196

Illustrator: Ron Wheeler
Editor: Christy Allen

Printed in the United States of America

These pages may be copied.

Permission is granted to the buyer of this book to reproduce, duplicate or photocopy these materials for use with students in Sunday school or Bible teaching classes.

Rainbow Books

Rainbow Publishers • P.O. Box 261129 • San Diego, CA 92196

Contents

Memory Verse Index

Old Testament

New Testament

Introduction

All you need are scissors, glue and crayons to use *Cut, Color and Paste* — a Bible-teaching format designed for the learning abilities of preschoolers. On the left side of each two-page lesson you will find a top section to help you teach concepts. A memory verse, Bible story reference, talk points and discussion questions will guide you in presenting the scriptural message to your students.

Below the teaching portion are illustrations that the children cut out and glue to the larger illustration on the right. Discuss where the pieces could be glued, but also allow the children to select where they want to place them. Remember to provide crayons or markers for the students to color the picture! The finished project will serve as an ideal take-home sheet to assist parents in understanding your lesson topics so they can review them with their children.

As the children work on the activity, discuss the questions, which are designed to elicit the children's feelings or make them think about an aspect of God's love. In this way, the questions take important ideas from the Bible and help the children concretely incorporate them into their lives. And that is your goal as a teacher: to make God's love and the Bible come alive.

Apothecary

Read

About anointing oil in Exodus 30:22-31

Say

In biblical days anointing oil was very expensive and valuable, so anointing something with the oil showed the high value placed on it. This type of oil was only used for religious objects or on people approved by God. Perfume and sweet smelling oils were also used for religious ceremonies. The person who made the oil was called an apothecary. Today, we buy perfume and oils to make us smell good or to use in baths.

Ask

1. Who told Moses how to make the anointing oil? (the Lord)
2. Where do we go to get perfume today? (a store)

Activity

Have the children color and cut out the flasks of perfume ingredients. They should glue several on the apothecary's table and one in the apothecary's hand.

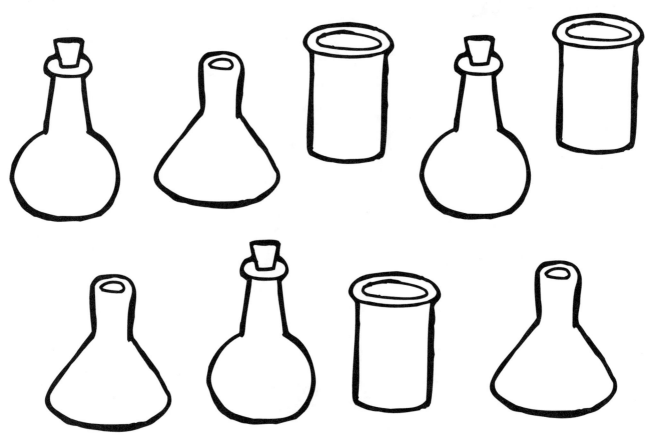

Apothecary

Make these into a sacred anointing oil,
a fragrant blend, the work of a perfumer.
Exodus 30:25

Astronomer

Read

About the Magi in Matthew 2:1-12

Say

Astronomers are people who study the stars and planets. In biblical times Magi or wise men studied the stars. When Jesus was born, a new star appeared in the sky. The Magi followed the new star and found Jesus.

Ask

1. Who followed the new star? (the Magi)
2. Who did the Magi find when they followed the star? (Jesus)

Activity

Have the children color and cut out the stars. They should glue the stars in the sky.

Astronomer

When they saw the star,
they were overjoyed.
Matthew 2:10

Athlete

Memory Verse

Similarly, if anyone competes as an athlete, he does not receive the victor's crown unless he competes according to the rules.

2 Timothy 2:5

Read

About a race in 1 Corinthians 9:24-27

Say

Athletes have to eat correctly and train a long time to win races. Then if the athletes follow the rules of the race, they might win a crown or a medal. Paul tells us to be good Christians we also have to train a long time by studying about God. Then if we follow the rules found in the Bible we can win the crown of eternal life through Jesus Christ.

Ask

1. Who has to train a long time to win races? (athletes)
2. Who trains to be good Christians? (We do.)

Activity

Have the children color and cut out the athletes. They should glue the athletes on the page competing in a race.

Athlete

Similarly, if anyone competes as an athlete, he does not receive the victor's crown unless he competes according to the rules.
2 Timothy 2:5

Baker

Memory Verse

When the chief baker saw that Joseph had given a favorable interpretation, he said to Joseph, "I too had a dream: On my head were three baskets of bread."

Genesis 40:16

Read

About the baker in Genesis 40:1-17

Say

God gives some people the talent to bake. A baker is a person who makes bread, cupcakes or cookies. In biblical days bakers worked for kings, making their bread. Today, bakers usually work in a store called a bakery and sell cookies, pies, cakes and bread.

Ask

1. In the story, who did the baker make bread for? (Pharaoh)
2. Have you ever been to a bakery? What did you buy?

Activity

Have the children cut out the loaves of bread and paste them in the basket on the baker's head.

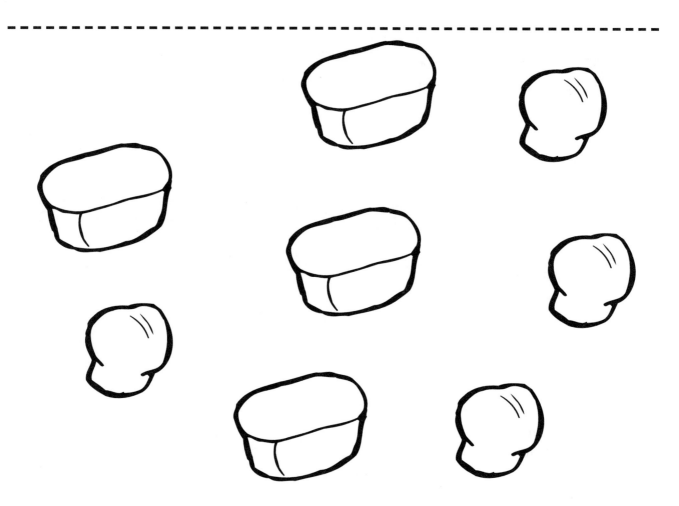

14

Baker

When the chief baker saw that Joseph had given a favorable interpretation,
he said to Joseph, "I too had a dream: On my head were three baskets of bread."
Genesis 40:16

Banker

Read

About Jesus at the temple in Matthew 21:12-13

Say

Bankers are people who work with money. In biblical days money changers were like bankers. In the story, the money changers were working in the church doing business instead of worshipping God. Jesus was very angry. When we are at work we should be doing business. When we are at church we should be praying and worshipping God.

Ask

1. What did Jesus do to the moneychangers? (overturned their tables)
2. What are we supposed to do in church? (pray and worship God)

Activity

Have the children color and cut out the coins and tables. They should glue the tables upside-down and the coins all over the ground.

Banker

*He scattered the coins of the money changers
and overturned their tables.*
John 2:15

Brazier

Memory Verse

Zillah also had a son, Tubal-Cain, who forged all kinds of tools out of bronze and iron.

Genesis 4:22

Read

An ax head floats in 2 Kings 6:1-7.

Say

A brazier was someone who made tools like axes, spears, hammers and nails out of iron or bronze. In biblical days if someone wanted an ax he asked the brazier to make it for him. Today, axes, hammers and nails are made in factories and we go to the hardware store to buy them.

Ask

1. Why did people need axes in biblical days? (to cut down trees)
2. What do we use hammers and nails for today?

Activity

Have the children color and cut out the tools. They should glue the tools in the brazier's hand as he works and elsewhere in the picture.

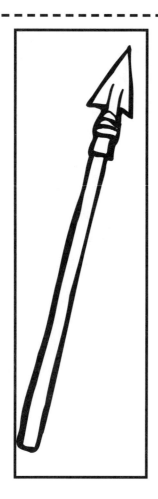

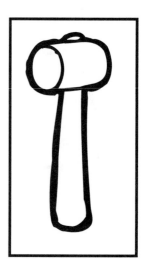

Brazier

Zillah also had a son, Tubal-Cain, who forged
all kinds of tools out of bronze and iron.
Genesis 4:22

Builder

Read

The tower of Babel in Genesis 11:1-9

Say

God didn't want people to try to get to heaven by building a tower. There is only one way to get to heaven.

Ask

1. Do you know how to get to heaven? (through Jesus Christ, our savior)
2. What do builders build today?

Activity

Have the children color and cut out the bricks. They should glue them on the tower.

Builder

Come, let us build ourselves a city,
with a tower that reaches to the heavens.
Genesis 11:4

Carpenter

Read

About some carpenters following God's instructions in Exodus 25:9-22

Say

Carpenters are people who build things out of wood like tables and chairs. In the story, God gave the carpenters exact instructions to build a chest. God also gives us exact instructions how to build our lives.

Ask

1. What did God instruct the carpenters to build in the story? (a chest)
2. Where are God's instructions for our lives found? (in the Bible)

Activity

Have the children color and cut out the wood. They should glue the pieces of wood into the carpenter's hands.

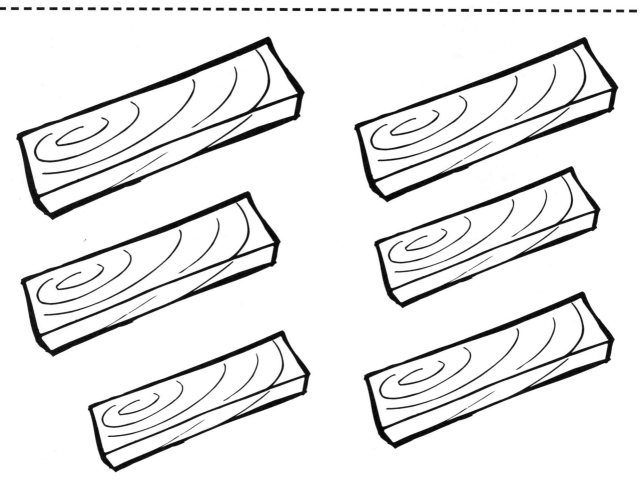

Carpenter

Isn't this the carpenter?
Mark 6:3

Cook

Read

About a meal cooked for special visitors in Genesis 18:1-14

Say

God gives some people the talent to cook. A cook is someone who prepares food for people to eat. In the memory verse, Jesus tells us giving someone food is one way to serve the Lord. In the story, Sara cooked a meal and served the Lord and two angels. God is happy when we serve Him and His children with our talents.

Ask

1. What did Sara cook for the angels? (bread, a calf, curds and milk)
2. What would you serve the Lord?

Activity

Have the children color and cut out the food. They should glue the food to the plates.

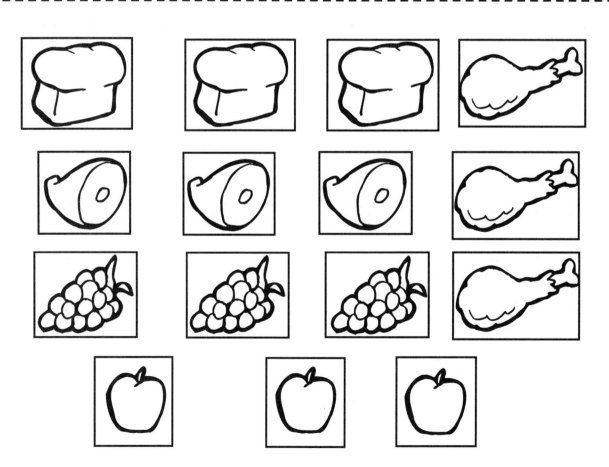

Cook

For I was hungry and you
gave me something to eat.
Matthew 25:35

Dancer

Read

How to praise God in Psalm 150

Say

Dancers are people who move to music. Ballet dancers, tap dancers and jazz dancers are some of the different kinds of dancers there are. Dancing can also be used to praise the Lord.

Ask

1. What are ways to praise the Lord? (dancing, music, praying, etc.)
2. Who can praise the Lord? (Everyone.)

Activity

Have the children color and cut out the different types of dancers. They should glue them on the stage.

Dancer

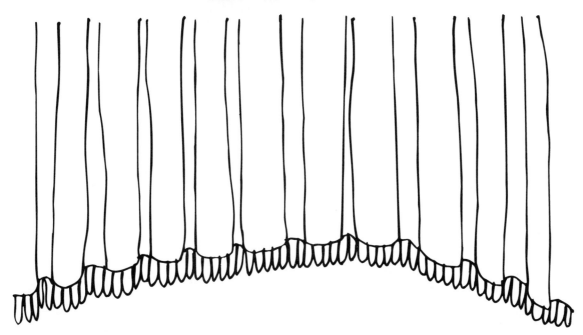

Praise him with tambourine and dancing.
Psalm 150:4

Doctor

Memory Verse

Jesus said, "It is not the healthy who need a doctor, but the sick."

Matthew 9:12

Read

About Jesus healing sick people in Luke 4:38-40

Say

God creates people like doctors and nurses who like to take care of the sick. A doctor is a person who heals us when we are sick or hurt. Doctors use medicine to heal people. Jesus healed many people of their diseases, too. But Jesus used God's power to heal people.

Ask

1. Who did Jesus heal in the story? (Simon's mother-in-law and many other people)
2. Why do you go to the doctor?

Activity

Have the children color and cut out Simon's mother-in-law. They should glue her to the bed.

Doctor

Jesus said, "It is not the healthy
who need a doctor, but the sick."
Matthew 9:12

Doorkeeper

Memory Verse

I would rather be a doorkeeper in the house of my God than dwell in the tents of the wicked.

Psalm 84:10

Read

About a lovely dwelling place in Psalm 84:1-12

Say

A doorkeeper is a person who stands near the front door of a building and lets people in or out. The doorkeeper watches to make sure no harm comes to the people who live in the building, just like God watches over us.

Ask

1. In the psalm, whose house was the doorkeeper watching? (God's)
2. Who watches over us and our homes? (God)

Activity

Have the children color and cut out the doorkeeper. They should glue him in front of the palace door.

Doorkeeper

*I would rather be a doorkeeper in the house of my God
than dwell in the tents of the wicked.*
Psalm 84:10

Draftsman

Memory Verse

Now, son of man, take a clay tablet,
put it in front of you and draw
the city of Jerusalem on it.
Ezekiel 4:1

Read

About the work of a draftsman in Ezekiel 4:1-3

Say

A draftsman is a person who draws the plans or blueprints for a building or a city. The draftsman then gives it to the builders so they have instructions to follow when they build.

Ask

1. What city did Ezekiel draw? (Jerusalem)
2. What did Ezekiel draw on? (a clay tablet)

Activity

Have the children color and cut out the clay tablet. They should glue the clay tablet in front of Ezekiel.

Draftsman

Now, son of man, take a clay tablet, put it in front of you
and draw the city of Jerusalem on it.
Ezekiel 4:1

Embroiderer

Memory Verse

He has filled them with skill to do all kinds of work as craftsmen, designers, embroiderers.

Exodus 35:35

Read

About Bezalel and Oholiab in Exodus 35:30-35

Say

Embroidery is sewing with colored thread on fabric to make pictures. God gives some people special skills to work with threads and fabrics to make beautiful pictures.

Ask

1. What color of yarn were the men in the story using? (blue, purple, scarlet)
2. Who gives people special skills to use for His glory? (God)

Activity

Before class, use a hole punch to make holes where indicated. Have the children color the picture. Cut a piece of yarn 18" long for each child. Thread the yarn through a plastic sewing needle. Let the children sew the yarn into the dots on the picture.

Embroiderer

*He has filled them with skill to do all kinds of work as
craftsmen, designers, embroiderers.*
Exodus 35:35

armer

Memory Verse

A farmer went out to sow his seed.
Matthew 13:3

Read

The parable of the sower in Matthew 13:3-9 and 18-23

Say

A farmer is a person who plants and grows crops. In this story Jesus was talking about people who hear the Word of God. Some people hear the Word of God and ignore it. Some people hear the Word of God and follow it for awhile then forget about it. And some people hear the Word of God and it grows in their hearts and changes their lives.

Ask

1. Where did the farmer sow the seed? (the path, rocky places, thorns and good soil)
2. Have you ever been to a farm? What did you see?

Activity

Have the children color and cut out the farmer as he sows seeds. They should glue the farmer in the scene.

Farmer

A farmer went out to sow his seed.
Matthew 13:3

Fisherman

Memory Verse

*"Come, follow me," Jesus said, "and
I will make you fishers of men."*
Matthew 4:19

Read

About fishermen in Luke 5:1-11

Say

Fishermen are people who gather fish and sell them for food. Jesus wanted to teach the fishermen to gather people and teach them about God.

Ask

1. In the story, what happened to the nets after Jesus told the men to go fishing? (They broke.)
   Why? (too many fish)
2. Have you ever been fishing? What did you catch?

Activity

Have the children color and cut out the fish. They should glue the fish into the nets, then draw the sail on the boat.

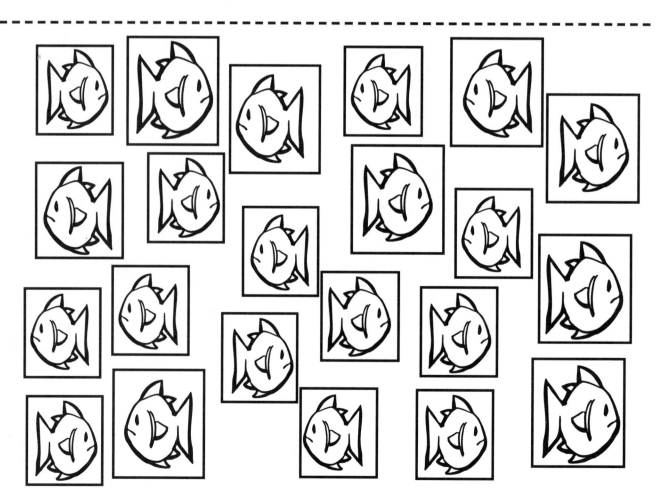

Fisherman

"Come, follow me," Jesus said, *"and
I will make you fishers of men."*
Matthew 4:19

Gardener

Read

About a gardener in Genesis 2:8-15

Say

God made beautiful flowers and trees. God made vegetables and fruit to grow. God also provided people, called gardeners, who like to grow fruit and vegetables and take care of gardens. God provides for all His creations: people, animals, trees and flowers. God will provide for you, too.

Ask

1. What was in the Garden of Eden? (trees and rivers)
2. Who provided a gardener to take care of the Garden of Eden? (God)

Activity

Have the children color and cut out the flowers, fruit and corn. They should glue the flowers to the flower stems, the fruit to the trees and the corn to the stalks.

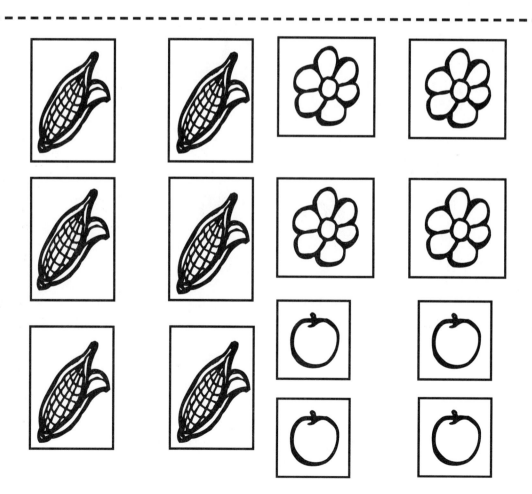

Gardener

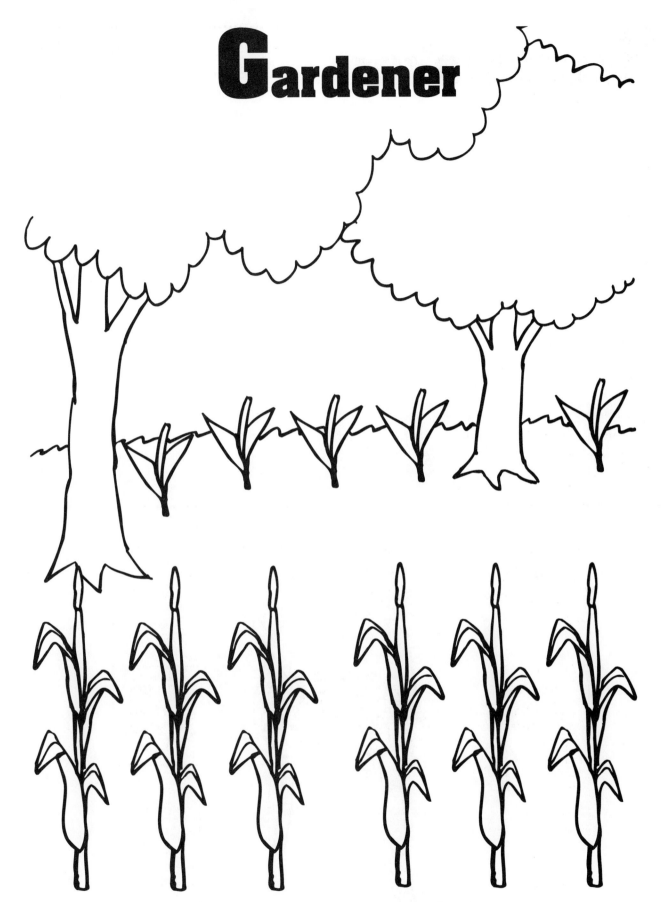

*The Lord God took the man and put him in
the Garden of Eden to work it and take care of it.*
Genesis 2:15

Homemaker

Read

About a homemaker in Proverbs 31:10-31

Say

A homemaker is a person who works in the home. She provides food, cleans, takes care of her family and conducts business as needed. Homemaking is a very hard job but a necessary one.

Ask

1. What is a wife of noble character worth? (more than rubies)
2. Name some of the things the homemaker in the story does. (sews, cooks, buys a field, etc.)

Activity

Have the children color and cut out the homemaker on this page. They should glue the homemaker in the scene.

Homemaker

She watches over the affairs of her household.
Proverbs 31:27

Hunter

Memory Verse
*Esau became a skillful hunter,
a man of the open country.*
Genesis 25:27

Read

About Jacob and Esau in Genesis 25:19-34

Say

A hunter is a person who goes into the woods or fields and hunts for deer or squirrels to eat. Long ago people had to hunt for their food. Today we can go to the supermarket to buy food. Some people still like to hunt for sport.

Ask

1. Who were the twins named in the story? (Jacob and Esau)
2. Which twin was the hunter? (Esau)

Activity

Have the children color and cut out Esau. They should glue Esau in the open country hunting.

Hunter

Esau became a skillful hunter,
a man of the open country.
Genesis 25:27

Innkeeper

Memory Verse

*The next day he took out two silver coins
and gave them to the innkeeper.*
Luke 10:35

Read

The Good Samaritan in Luke 10:30-37

Say

God provides places for people to stay when they are away from home. An innkeeper is a person who has rooms for people to stay in for the night while they are traveling. Today we stay in hotels and motels when we travel.

Ask

1. Where did the Samaritan take the injured man? (to the inn)
2. Have you ever stayed in a hotel or a motel?

Activity

Have the children color and cut out the beds. They should glue them in the rooms at the inn.

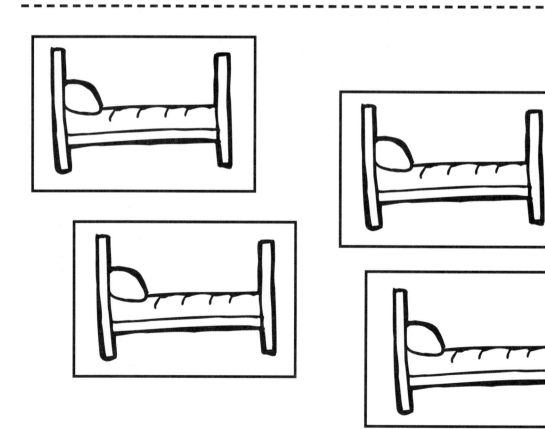

Innkeeper

The next day he took out two silver coins
and gave them to the innkeeper.
Luke 10:35

Jailer

Memory Verse

They were thrown into prison, and the jailer was commanded to guard them carefully.
Acts 16:23

Read

About the jailer in Acts 16:16-34

Say

A jailer is a person who guards prisoners. Paul and Silas were prisoners many times because they preached about Jesus. Even though they were in jail they praised God and sang hymns to Him. All the other prisoners listened and learned about God. The jailer wanted to learn more about God, too. Paul and Silas taught the jailer and his family about God and the jailer was filled with joy. No matter where we are, we can teach others about Jesus.

Ask

1. What happened while Paul and Silas were praying? (There was an earthquake.)
2. What do we have to do to be saved? (believe in the Lord Jesus)

Activity

Have the children color and cut out the jailer on his knees. They should glue the jailer in front of Paul and Silas in prison.

Jailer

*They were thrown into prison, and the jailer
was commanded to guard them carefully.*
Acts 16:23

Jeweler

Memory Verse

See, I have chosen Bezalel...
to cut and set stones.
Exodus 31:2,5

Read

About the work of a jeweler in Exodus 28:15-21

Say

A jeweler is a person that works with gold, silver and precious gems to make rings, necklaces, bracelets, etc. In the story God chose Bezalel to follow His instructions on certain jewelry God wanted made for the priests. God gives us special skills to use to honor Him.

Ask

1. What were the gems used on the breast piece? (see list are in Exodus 28:17-20)
2. Who did God choose to make the breast piece? (Bezalel)

Activity

Have the children color and cut out the gems. They should mount the gems on the breast piece.

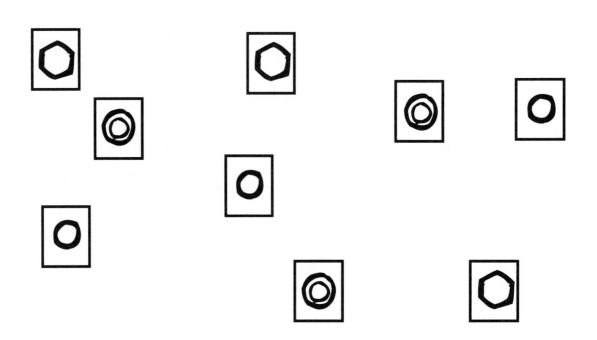

Jeweler

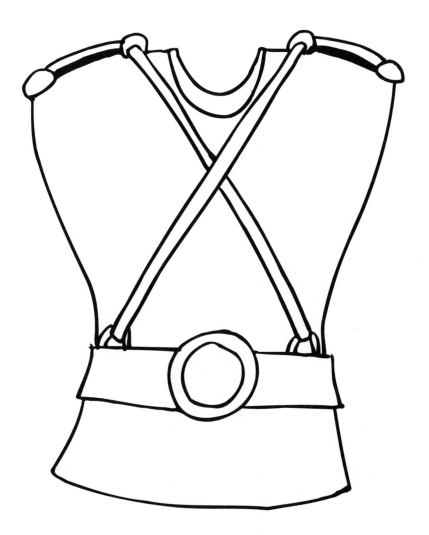

See, I have chosen Bezalel…
to cut and set stones.
Exodus 31:2,5

Judge

Memory Verse

Appoint judges and officials…
and they shall judge the people fairly.
Deuteronomy 16:18

Read

Some rules about being a judge in Deuteronomy 16:18-20

Say

God provides people to enforce the laws of the country. A judge is someone that listens to complaints between people and decides if a law has been broken. Judges send people to jail if they break the laws. Judges have to be fair to everyone.

Ask

1. In the story, what should the judges follow? (justice)
2. Is it hard to be fair to everyone all of the time?

Activity

Have the children color and cut out the judge. They should glue him in front of the two people in a dispute.

Judge

Appoint judges and officials…
and they shall judge the people fairly.
Deuteronomy 16:18

King

Read

David makes Solomon king in 1 Kings 1:28-40.

Say

Kings are men who rule a country. Kings are chosen by other kings. Our country, the U.S.A., has a president. Presidents are chosen by all of the people in the country who vote for him.

Ask

1. Who did David make king? (Solomon)
2. Who is our president?

Activity

Have the children color and cut out the robes and crown. They should glue the robes and crown on King Solomon.

King

Solomon your son shall be king after me,
and he will sit on my throne in my place.
1 Kings 1:30

Magician

Read

About Simon the magician in Acts 8:9-25

Say

Simon was a magician who did magic tricks that amazed people. But when the apostles came to town they performed miracles by the power of Jesus. These miracles were real, not magic tricks. Simon wanted to be able to perform miracles, too, not because he believed in Jesus, but because it would make Simon's magic better. The apostles were mad at Simon. God's power is not a magic trick to entertain people. God's power is real and can change the world.

Ask

1. Are magic tricks real? (no)
2. Whose power is real? (God's)

Activity

Have the children color and cut out Simon. They should glue Simon in the scene performing magic in front of the people.

Magician

*They followed him because he had amazed
them for a long time with his magic.*
Acts 8:11

Merchant

Memory Verse
*The merchants of Sheba
and Raamah traded with you.*
Ezekiel 27:22

Read

About merchants in Ezekiel 27:12-24

Say

A merchant is a person who buys and sells things to other people. In biblical days, merchants traveled from town to town buying items. Then the merchants would sell their wares in the marketplace. Today, merchants work in stores. If you need to buy something, you go to the store and buy it from a merchant.

Ask

1. What were some of the things bought and sold in the story? (silver, iron, tin, etc.)
2. Have you ever bought anything from a merchant? What?

Activity

Have the children color and cut out the wares below. They should glue each one on a merchant's table in the marketplace.

Merchant

*The merchants of Sheba
and Raamah traded with you.*
Ezekiel 27:22

59

Messenger

Memory Verse

See, I will send my messenger,
who will prepare the way before me.
Malachi 3:1

Read

About a messenger in Matthew 3:1-13

Say

A messenger is someone who brings people a message from someone else. In the story, John the Baptist was telling people the message that Jesus Christ was coming soon.

Ask

1. Who was the messenger? (John the Baptist)
2. Who did John the Baptist say was coming soon? (Jesus)

Activity

Have the children color and cut out John the Baptist. They should glue him in the Jordan River.

Messenger

See, I will send my messenger,
who will prepare the way before me.
Malachi 3:1

iner

Memory Verse

*He searches the farthest recesses
for ore in the blackest darkness.*
Job 28:3

Read

About miners in Job 28:1-11

Say

A miner is a person who goes under the ground and digs out gold or silver or diamonds or coal. It is very dark underground and miners have to use lights to see. Miners dig at the rock with a pick to get the minerals or gems out.

Ask

1. What are some things found in mines? (gold, silver, sapphires, etc.)
2. Where are mines? (underground)

Activity

Have the children color and cut out the miner. They should glue the miner in the mine.

Miner

He searches the farthest recesses
for ore in the blackest darkness.
Job 28:3

Missionary

Memory Verse

Set apart for me Barnabas and Saul for the work to which I have called them.

Acts 13:2

Read

About the work of a missionary in Acts 13:13-42

Say

A missionary is a person who travels to foreign lands to tell people the Good News that Jesus died for our sins. Paul was picked by God to be a missionary. Paul traveled to many different lands spreading the Good News.

Ask

1. What is the Good News? (Jesus died for our sins.)
2. Who traveled with Paul? (Barnabas)

Activity

Have the children color and cut out Paul and Barnabas. They should glue them speaking in the synagogue.

Missionary

*Set apart for me Barnabas and Saul
for the work to which I have called them*
Acts 13:2

Musician

Read

About praising God in Psalm 149:1-5

Say

A musician is a person who plays an instrument like a piano, harp or flute. God likes to hear music. One way to praise God is to play an instrument or sing a song.

Ask

1. In the psalm, what instruments are the musicians using? (tambourine and harp)
2. What are other ways to praise the Lord? (singing, dancing, praying)

Activity

Have the children color and cut out the musical instruments. They should glue them around the musician.

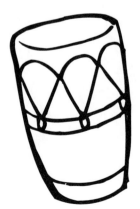

Musician

*Make music to him with
tambourine and harp.*
Psalm 149:3

Potter

Memory Verse

Like clay in the hand of the potter,
so are you in my hand.

Jeremiah 18:6

Read

About the potter in Jeremiah 18:1-6

Say

A potter is someone who makes vases, bowls and pots out of clay. In the story, the potter molded the clay to make a special pot. God told Jeremiah that God molds us into special people.

Ask

1. What did the potter use to make pots? (clay)
2. What did the potter use to shape the pot? (his hands)

Activity

Have the children color and cut out the pots and bowls below. They should glue the pots around the potter. Remind the children to glue a pot on the potter's wheel.

Potter

Like clay in the hand of the potter,
so are you in my hand.
Jeremiah 18:6

Priest

Memory Verse

Zechariah's division was on duty and he was serving as priest before God.

Luke 1:8

Read

About a priest in Luke 1:5-10

Say

A priest is a person who leads the church in worshipping God and teaching others about God. A minister is like a priest. Some churches have ministers and some churches have priests.

Ask

1. What was the name of the priest in the story? (Zechariah)
2. What is your pastor's or priest's name?

Activity

Have the children color and cut out the priest. They should glue him burning the incense.

Priest

*Zechariah's division was on duty and
he was serving as priest before God.*
Luke 1:8

Prophet

Read

About the prophet in Deuteronomy 18:14-22

Say

In biblical days, prophets were people who spoke the words of God. Prophets told people what God wanted them to know. Today, we can find what God wants us to know in the Bible.

Ask

1. Whose words does the prophet tell the people? (God's)
2. Where do we find God's words today? (in the Bible)

Activity

Have the children color and cut out the puzzle pieces. They should glue them together to make a prophet on the mountain.

Prophet

I will raise up for them a prophet.
Deuteronomy 18:18

Sailor

Memory Verse

All the sailors were afraid and each cried out to his own god.

Jonah 1:5

Read

About the sailors in Jonah 1:1-17

Say

Sailors are people who sail ships in the ocean. The sailors in the story were afraid of the storm. They prayed to false gods to save them. The false gods could not stop the storm. Only the one true God could calm the storm and save the sailors. When the sea became calm, the sailors thanked God and worshipped Him.

Ask

1. Who ran away from God? (Jonah)
2. Who learned to worship the one true God? (the sailors)

Activity

Have the children color and cut out the frightened sailors. They should glue them on the ship.

Sailor

All the sailors were afraid and each cried out to his own god.
Jonah 1:5

Servant

Read

Jesus washes His disciples' feet in John 13:1-17.

Say

A servant is a person who does whatever his master tells him to do. A servant cooks and cleans. Jesus is our Lord, yet He washed His disciples' feet, just like a servant. Jesus told His disciples and us that no matter how important you are, you still have to serve others. If you serve others, you will be blessed.

Ask

1. Whose feet did Jesus wash? (the disciples')
2. What can you do to serve others?

Activity

Have the children color and cut out the disciples. They should glue them around Jesus.

Servant

I tell you the truth, no servant
is greater than his master.
John 13:16

Shepherd

Memory Verse

And there were shepherds living out in the fields nearby, keeping watch over their flocks at night.

Luke 2:8

Read

About the shepherds and the angels in Luke 2:8-20

Say

Shepherds are people who take care of sheep. One night, some shepherds were watching their sheep when angels appeared. The angels came to tell the shepherds the Good News: Jesus Christ, our Savior, was born!

Ask

1. What did the shepherds see? (angels)
2. What was the Good News the angels told the shepherds? (Jesus was born.)

Activity

Have the children color and cut out the shepherds. They should glue them in the fields as they listen to the angels.

Shepherd

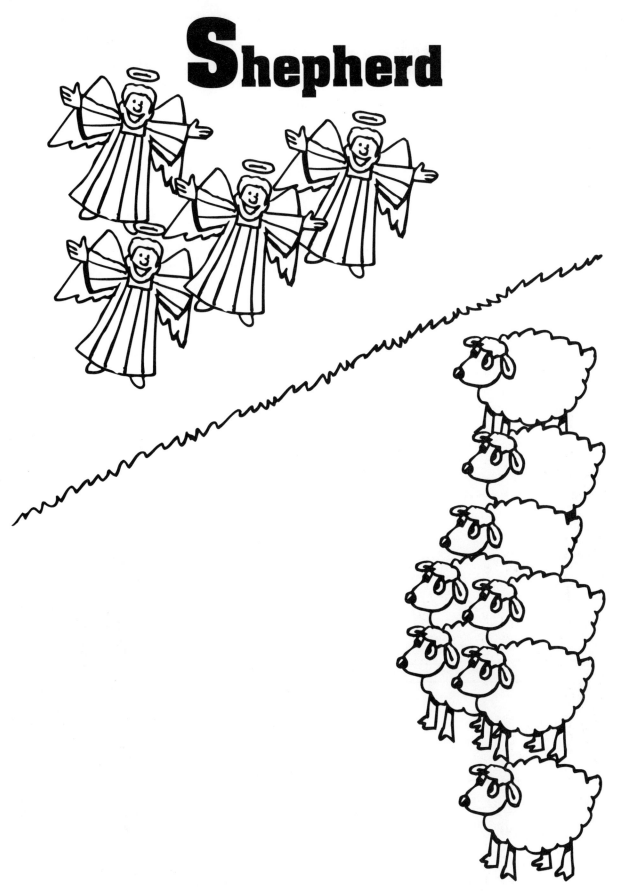

*And there were shepherds living out in the fields nearby,
keeping watch over their flocks at night.*
Luke 2:8

Shipbuilder

Memory Verse
Your builders brought your beauty to perfection.
Ezekiel 27:4

Read

About building ships in Ezekiel 27:3-9

Say

A shipbuilder is a person who builds big boats. In the story, the boats of Tyre were built from the finest woods. They had linen sails and decks made of ivory. The ships of Tyre must have been very beautiful.

Ask

1. Where were these beautiful ships from? (Tyre)
2. Have you ever been on a ship? What did it look like?

Activity

Have the children color and cut out the ships. They should glue the ships on the ocean.

Shipbuilder

Your builders brought your
beauty to perfection.
Ezekiel 27:4

Soldier

Memory Verse

*Endure hardship with us like
a good soldier of Christ Jesus.*
2 Timothy 2:3

Read

About soldiers for Jesus in 2 Timothy 2:1-4

Say

A soldier is someone in an army who fights for and protects what he or she believes in. Soldiers of Jesus Christ fight evil and protect the Word of God so that the Good News can be spread to everyone. The Good News is that Jesus died for our sins.

Ask

1. What is the Good News? (Jesus died for our sins.)
2. Where do we find the Word of God? (in the Bible)

Activity

Have the children draw their faces on the soldier, then color and cut out the soldier. They should glue the soldier on Jesus' army.

Soldier

*Endure hardship with us like
a good soldier of Christ Jesus.*
2 Timothy 2:3

Spinner

Memory Verse

Every skilled woman spun with her hands and brought what she had spun — blue, purple or scarlet yarn or fine linen.

Exodus 35:25

Read

About bringing offerings to the Lord in Exodus 35:20-26

Say

A spinner is someone who takes wool from sheep or goats and spins it on a spinning wheel and turns the wool into yarn. The yarn is used to make sweaters, socks, hats, etc. In the story, everyone wanted to bring something to God to help build the tabernacle. Some people brought wool they had spun. God is happy when we bring Him our gifts.

Ask

1. What color was the yarn the women brought to God? (blue, purple, scarlet)
2. What gift can you bring to God?

Activity

Have the children color and cut out the spinning wheels. They should glue the spinning wheels so that one is in front of each spinner.

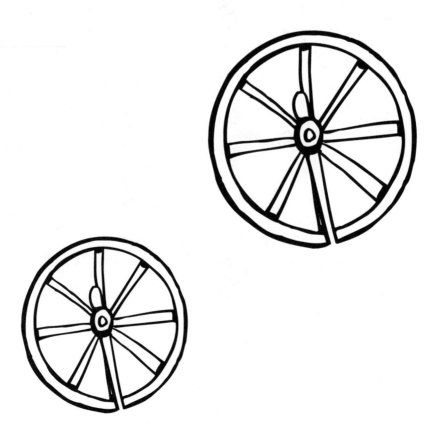

Spinner

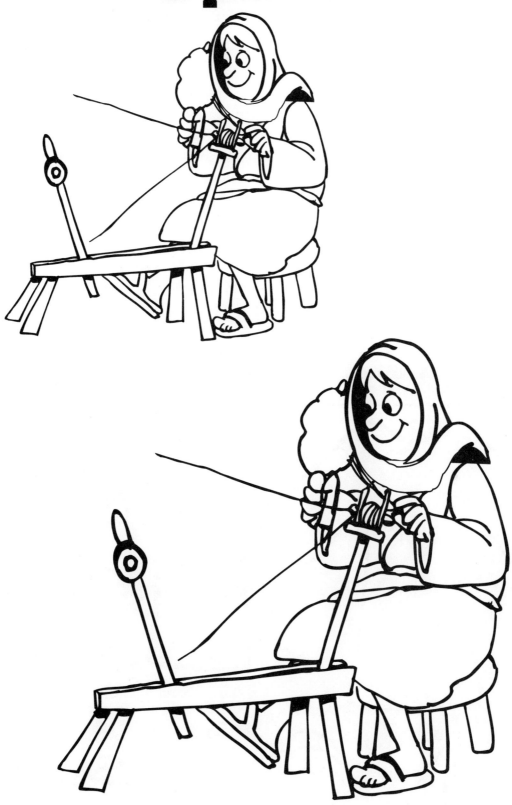

Every skilled woman spun with her hands and brought what she had spun —
blue, purple or scarlet yarn or fine linen.
Exodus 35:25

Tailor

Read

About tailors in Exodus 28:1-5

Say

Tailors are people who sew fabric together to make clothes. God gives some people special talents to make beautiful clothes. God gives each of us a special talent that we can use to serve Him.

Ask

1. Whom were the tailors making clothes for? (Aaron and his sons)
2. What is your special talent that you can use to serve God?

Activity

Have the children color and cut out the breast piece, apron, robe, tunic, turban and sash on this page. They should glue the clothes on Aaron.

Tailor

*Tell all the skilled men to whom I have given wisdom
in such matters that they are to make garments for Aaron.*
Exodus 28:3

Tax Collector

Memory Verse

After this, Jesus went out and saw a tax collector by the name of Levi sitting at his tax booth. "Follow me," Jesus said to him.

Luke 5:27

Read

The calling of Levi in Luke 5:27-32

Say

A tax collector is a person who collects tax money from people. In the story, no one liked the tax collectors because they thought the tax collectors stole some of the money. People called the tax collectors sinners. But Jesus loves everyone, even liars and thieves. Jesus came to save sinners and teach them to do right.

Ask

1. What did Levi do after Jesus called him? (left everything and followed Jesus)
2. Does Jesus love everyone? (yes)

Activity

Have the children color and cut out the coins and money bags. They should glue them on the tax collector's table.

Tax Collector

*After this, Jesus went out and saw a tax collector by the name of Levi
sitting at his tax booth. "Follow me," Jesus said to him.*
Luke 5:27

Tentmaker

Read

A warning against idleness in 2 Thessalonians 3:6-14

Say

A tentmaker is a person who sews cloth together to make tents. In Paul's day, many people lived in tents. Besides spreading the Word of God, Paul worked as a tentmaker. In the story, Paul reminds people to work to earn money for food and to take care of their families.

Ask

1. What kind of work does your mother or father do?
2. What kind of work do you want to do when you grow up?

Activity

Have the children color and cut out Paul. They should glue him on the page as he works on a tent with his friends.

Tentmaker

Because he was a tentmaker as they were, he stayed and worked with them.
Acts 18:3

Watchman

Memory Verse

*Son of man, I have made you
a watchman for the house of Israel.*
Ezekiel 33:7

Read

Ezekiel as a watchman in Ezekiel 33:1-7

Say

A watchman is a person who guards an area to make sure no intruders come in. In biblical days, there were walls around cities to protect them. The watchman stayed in a tower near the wall and kept a lookout for intruders. If he saw someone trying to invade the city he blew a trumpet to warn the people in the city. Today, security guards are like watchmen. They patrol buildings or property to keep robbers away.

Ask

1. What did the watchman in the story use to warn the people? (a trumpet)
2. Who is like a watchman today? (a security guard)

Activity

Have the children color and cut out the trumpet and watchman. They should glue the watchman in the tower and glue the trumpet in his hand.

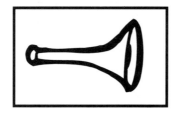

Watchman

Son of man, I have made you
a watchman for the house of Israel.
Ezekiel 33:7

Writer

Memory Verse

*This is what the Lord, the God of Israel, says:
"Write in a book all the words I
have spoken to you."*
Jeremiah 30:2

Read

Any story of your choice in the Bible

Say

Writers are people who write stories or books. The Bible was written by many different writers.
God inspired people like Matthew, Mark, Luke and John to write what Jesus did when He
was here on earth. Now we can read stories about Jesus in our Bibles.

Ask

1. What is your favorite story in the Bible?
2. What is your favorite story not in the Bible?

Activity

Have the children color and cut out the writer. They should glue the writer working on his book.

Writer

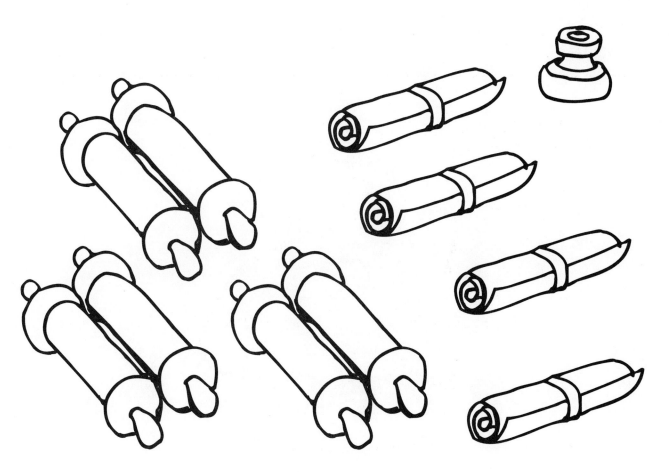

This is what the Lord, the God of Israel, says:
"Write in a book all the words I have spoken to you."
Jeremiah 30:2